To Maher

Wailana the Waterbug

Story by Greg Barrett & Jane Hopkins
Adapted by Lisa Matsumoto
Paintings by Michael Furuya

Alana Dung Research Foundation

First published in 1999 by the *Alana Dung Research Foundation*,
765 Amana Street #503, Honolulu, Hawai'i 96814 USA

Printed in Korea
Second Printing, 2005
ISBN: 1-56647-301-2

Book design: Terry M. Hubbard

MUTUAL PUBLISHING

This book is dedicated to

Spencer

for his love and understanding during his sister's illness

and

the 30,788 residents who became bone marrow registrants

and the many others in Hawai'i who displayed

an outpouring of the Aloha Spirit

Our projects begin as a thought … a seed

Over time, caring individuals provide love, encouragement, and warmth

The seed grows and becomes much more than anything we could envision.

This project was no different

It began with our need to share the story of transformation with others

…that death is never the end but rather the beginning.

A team of gifted individuals shared our vision and willingly

and generously gave of themselves to make this project a reality:

Alvin Chung spearheaded the effort,

Greg Barrett used his creative genius to express our theme in a narrative form,

Jane Hopkins contributed a Hawaiian flair,

Lisa Matsumoto gave it its final sparkle,

Michael Furuya magnificently added color and animation to the text,

Terry Hubbard with his keen sense of design put it all together,

Ric Noyle graciously gave his photographic talents,

Janice Shimokihara and Brian Onaga at HonBlue maintained the brilliant colors,

Gay Wong and Bennett Hymer, the technical experts, guided us

and believed this project would be more than a dream.

To the numerous others who uplift us in countless ways, we are grateful.

Your enthusiastic support propels us forward.

Of course, Alana continues to provide the inspiration and fuels the burning desire we have to support

those whose efforts are directed toward finding ways to combat childhood suffering and disease.

Adelia and Stephen Dung

Little Alana Dung was in the bud of life when leukemia took her from this earth. She was three and a half years old, her life a blink in time. Yet the impact and awareness she generated continues through the work of family and friends through the Alana Dung Research Foundation. *Wailana the Waterbug* is a project of the Foundation, a burgeoning non profit organization that exists solely to foster miracles. All proceeds from the book will be donated by the Foundation to clinical studies and research aimed at improving the quality of life for sick children–improving their treatment and eventually preventing disease. In many ways, *Wailana the Waterbug* is Alana's story. It's the story of any child taken from us; immense grief tempered by the joy of knowing a spirit received the wings of eternity. Alana's battle with leukemia and her family's resolve to save her is legend in Hawai'i. In a staggering show of aloha, 30,788 people attempted to help by joining the Hawaii Bone Marrow Donor Registry. This unbridled rush to help a sick girl nearly tripled the size of the seven-year old registry.

Following a successful bone marrow transplant, and later a relapse, Alana passed away as she drifted in and out of sleep on October 14, 1997. A slight smile graced her face. She appeared at peace. At her funeral, the story of how a waterbug is transformed into a dragonfly–flying free into the freshness of another world–helped lift a mood that was so heavy from the loss. That day, Alana's uncle Alvin Chung told friends and family, crowded into the Thurston Memorial Chapel on the campus of Punahou School, that Alana had taught her family three very important lessons. Appreciate the beauty of each day. Embrace the love of family and friends. And believe in the power of prayer. It was with that spirit that this project was conceived.

For more information about the Alana Dung Research Foundation or to order additional books, please write:
765 Amana Street, Suite 503 Honolulu, HI 96814 or visit the website at alanadungfoundation.org.

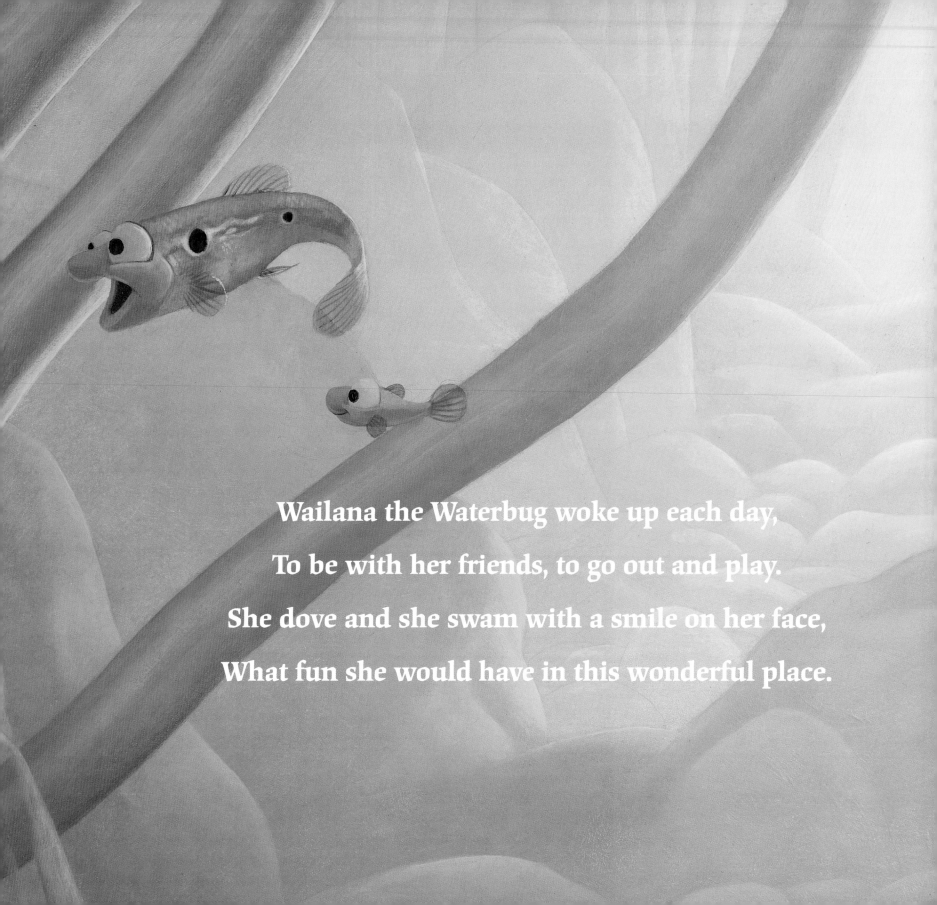

Wailana the Waterbug woke up each day,

To be with her friends, to go out and play.

She dove and she swam with a smile on her face,

What fun she would have in this wonderful place.

Swimming about, she would bubble with glee

Oh, how she loved all the sights she would see

Wherever she swam, a rainbow would follow-

Past reeds, over rocks and through logs that were hollow.

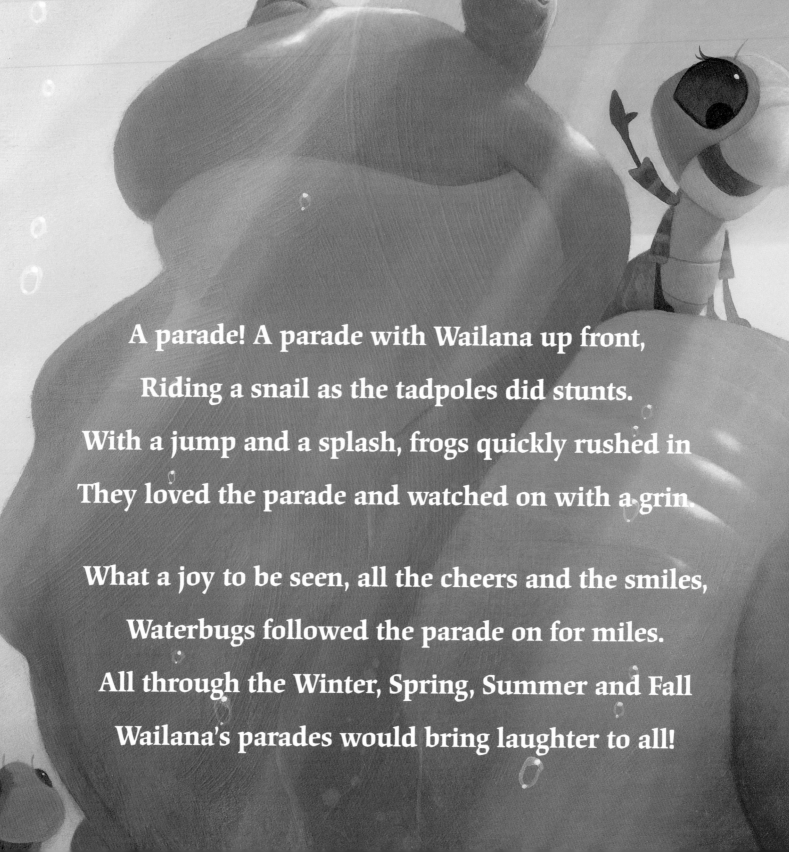

A parade! A parade with Wailana up front,

Riding a snail as the tadpoles did stunts.

With a jump and a splash, frogs quickly rushed in

They loved the parade and watched on with a grin.

What a joy to be seen, all the cheers and the smiles,

Waterbugs followed the parade on for miles.

All through the Winter, Spring, Summer and Fall

Wailana's parades would bring laughter to all!

Along with her friends, she would practice each day

Perfecting her dance for the water ballet.

With a leap and a spin, she heard cheers from the crowd

Her parents just gleamed and they felt very proud.

Then, one rainy day, she awoke feeling blue,

How her stomach had ached and all her joints too.

Family and friends came from far and wide

To gather around her and be by her side.

The elders would whisper and bow down their heads.

They knew what would happen and started to dread.

Wailana was calm and didn't feel fear.

She wasn't afraid because love was so near.

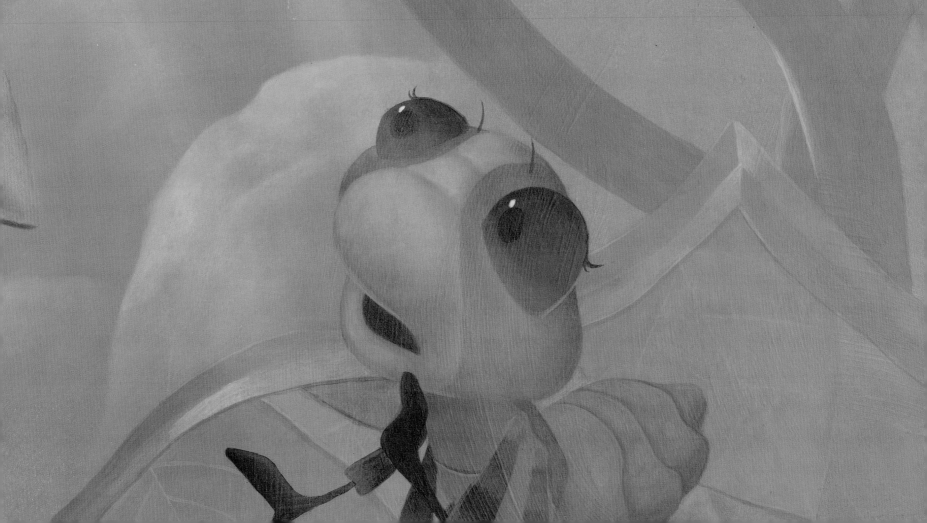

Stories were shared from long, long ago,

About others who changed and then had to go.

After leaving the pond, they would head for the sky,

While all understood, they could not explain why.

Unable to play,
she would rest every day
Her friends gathered near her
and started to pray,

"Wailana, please join us
and lead the parade." But Wailana
now knew that her time
would soon fade.

Surrounded by loved ones, it soon was the day

To say her good-byes and be on her way.

Wailana was sad but she knew in her heart

The time had now come for her new life to start.

Later that night by the light of the moon

She prepared for the change that would take place soon.

When all of a sudden, wings magically grew,

Reflecting the moon beams that shone brightly through.

A rainbow of colors danced in the light,

She never had seen such a glorious sight!

Then turning around, she let out a giggle

While making her dragonfly tail start to wiggle!

She flapped her new wings, testing them out,

Then found herself quickly floating about.

Flying higher and higher, she looked down below,

At her lily pad home and called out, "Hello."

Feeling much better, she soon learned to soar,

Over rainbows, through forests she soon would explore.

Her sadness was gone, she no longer felt blue,

She soon again found all the joy she once knew.

Now a beautiful dragonfly high up above,

Wailana would watch over those that she loved.

What fun she now had, through clouds she would fly,

Leading parades with her friends in the sky!

Wailana the Waterbug

Alana Dung Research Foundation